M.A.S.H.

WHO: _____ **DATE:** _____

DWELLING
_____

MANSION

APARTMENT

SHACK

HOUSE

CITY
_____
_____
_____
_____

VEHICLE
_____
_____
_____
_____

SPOUSE
_____
_____
_____
_____

OCCUPATION
_____
_____
_____
_____

SPOUSE'S OCCUPATION
_____
_____
_____

INCOME
_____
_____
_____

No. OF KIDS
_____
_____
_____

TYPE OF PET
_____
_____
_____

HONEYMOON DESTINATION
_____
_____

(FILL-IN CATEGORY)
_____
_____
_____

FOLLOW ZIGZAG UNTIL
A FRIEND SAYS "STOP."
COUNT THE NUMBER OF
DOTS YOU CROSS.

NUMBER:

M.A.S.H.

DWELLING

MANSION

APARTMENT

SHACK

HOUSE

SPOUSE

OCCUPATION

SPOUSE'S OCCUPATION

INCOME

CITY

FOLLOW ZIGZAG UNTIL
A FRIEND SAYS "STOP."
COUNT THE NUMBER OF
DOTS YOU CROSS.

NUMBER:

VEHICLE

No. OF KIDS

TYPE OF PET

HONEYMOON DESTINATION

(FILL-IN CATEGORY)

M.A.S.H.

DWELLING

MANSION

APARTMENT

SHACK

HOUSE

SPOUSE

OCCUPATION

SPOUSE'S OCCUPATION

INCOME

CITY

VEHICLE

No. OF KIDS

TYPE OF PET

HONEYMOON DESTINATION

(FILL-IN CATEGORY)

FOLLOW ZIGZAG UNTIL
A FRIEND SAYS "STOP."
COUNT THE NUMBER OF
DOTS YOU CROSS.

NUMBER:

M.A.S.H.

DWELLING

MANSION _____

APARTMENT _____

SHACK _____

HOUSE _____

CITY

_____

_____

_____

_____

VEHICLE

_____

_____

_____

_____

SPOUSE

_____

_____

_____

_____

No. OF KIDS

_____

_____

_____

OCCUPATION

_____

_____

_____

TYPE OF PET

_____

_____

_____

SPOUSE'S OCCUPATION

_____

_____

_____

HONEYMOON DESTINATION

_____

_____

_____

INCOME

_____

_____

_____

FOLLOW ZIGZAG UNTIL
A FRIEND SAYS "STOP."
COUNT THE NUMBER OF
DOTS YOU CROSS.

NUMBER:

(FILL-IN CATEGORY)

_____

_____

_____

M.A.S.H.

DWELLING

MANSION

APARTMENT

SHACK

HOUSE

CITY

VEHICLE

SPOUSE

No. OF KIDS

OCCUPATION

TYPE OF PET

SPOUSE'S OCCUPATION

HONEYMOON DESTINATION

INCOME

FOLLOW ZIGZAG UNTIL A FRIEND SAYS "STOP." COUNT THE NUMBER OF DOTS YOU CROSS.

NUMBER:

(FILL-IN CATEGORY)

M.A.S.H.

DWELLING

MANSION

APARTMENT

SHACK

HOUSE

CITY
_____
_____
_____
_____

VEHICLE
_____
_____
_____
_____

SPOUSE
_____
_____
_____
_____

No. OF KIDS
_____
_____
_____
_____

OCCUPATION
_____
_____
_____

TYPE OF PET
_____
_____
_____

SPOUSE'S OCCUPATION
_____
_____
_____

HONEYMOON DESTINATION
_____
_____
_____

INCOME
_____
_____
_____

FOLLOW ZIGZAG UNTIL A FRIEND SAYS "STOP." COUNT THE NUMBER OF DOTS YOU CROSS.

NUMBER:

(FILL-IN CATEGORY)
_____
_____
_____

M.A.S.H.

DWELLING

MANSION

APARTMENT

SHACK

HOUSE

SPOUSE

OCCUPATION

SPOUSE'S OCCUPATION

INCOME

CITY

FOLLOW ZIGZAG UNTIL
A FRIEND SAYS "STOP."
COUNT THE NUMBER OF
DOTS YOU CROSS.

NUMBER:

VEHICLE

No. OF KIDS

TYPE OF PET

HONEYMOON DESTINATION

(FILL-IN CATEGORY)

M.A.S.H.

WHO: _____

DATE: _____

DWELLING
MANSION
APARTMENT
SHACK
HOUSE

CITY

VEHICLE

SPOUSE

No. OF KIDS

OCCUPATION

TYPE OF PET

SPOUSE'S OCCUPATION

HONEYMOON DESTINATION

INCOME

FOLLOW ZIGZAG UNTIL
A FRIEND SAYS "STOP."
COUNT THE NUMBER OF
DOTS YOU CROSS.

NUMBER:

(FILL-IN CATEGORY)

M.A.S.H.

DWELLING

MANSION

APARTMENT

SHACK

HOUSE

CITY

VEHICLE

SPOUSE

No. OF KIDS

OCCUPATION

TYPE OF PET

SPOUSE'S OCCUPATION

HONEYMOON DESTINATION

INCOME

FOLLOW ZIGZAG UNTIL
A FRIEND SAYS "STOP."
COUNT THE NUMBER OF
DOTS YOU CROSS.

NUMBER:

(FILL-IN CATEGORY)

M.A.S.H.

DWELLING

MANSION _____

APARTMENT _____

SHACK _____

HOUSE _____

CITY

_____
_____
_____
_____

VEHICLE

_____
_____
_____
_____

SPOUSE

_____
_____
_____
_____

No. OF KIDS

_____
_____
_____

OCCUPATION

_____
_____
_____
_____

TYPE OF PET

_____
_____
_____

SPOUSE'S OCCUPATION

_____
_____
_____
_____

HONEYMOON DESTINATION

_____
_____
_____

INCOME

_____
_____
_____

FOLLOW ZIGZAG UNTIL
A FRIEND SAYS "STOP."
COUNT THE NUMBER OF
DOTS YOU CROSS.

NUMBER:

(FILL-IN CATEGORY)

_____
_____
_____

M.A.S.H.

DWELLING

MANSION

APARTMENT

SHACK

HOUSE

CITY

VEHICLE

SPOUSE

No. OF KIDS

OCCUPATION

TYPE OF PET

SPOUSE'S OCCUPATION

HONEYMOON DESTINATION

FOLLOW ZIGZAG UNTIL
A FRIEND SAYS "STOP."
COUNT THE NUMBER OF
DOTS YOU CROSS.

NUMBER:

INCOME

(FILL-IN CATEGORY)

M.A.S.H.

DWELLING

MANSION

APARTMENT

SHACK

HOUSE

CITY

VEHICLE

SPOUSE

No. OF KIDS

OCCUPATION

TYPE OF PET

SPOUSE'S OCCUPATION

HONEYMOON DESTINATION

FOLLOW ZIGZAG UNTIL
A FRIEND SAYS "STOP."
COUNT THE NUMBER OF
DOTS YOU CROSS.

NUMBER:

INCOME

(FILL-IN CATEGORY)

OUT AND ABOUT BINGO

COFFEE HOUSE	**CELL PHONE**	**BABY**	**SKYLINE**	**DOG**

CLOUD	**HEADPHONES**	**MAGAZINE**	**NEWSPAPER**	**BOTTLED WATER**

BILLBOARD	**SPEED SIGN**	**CAR**	**REST AREA**	**MOTORCYCLE**

BRIDGE	**BUS**	**SATELLITE DISH**	**LAKE**	**FLAG**

TRAFFIC CONE	**OUT OF STATE**	**GAS STATION**	**FOREST**	**POLICE CAR**

OUT AND ABOUT BINGO

COFFEE HOUSE	**CELL PHONE**	 **BABY**	 **SKYLINE**	 **DOG**
 **CLOUD**	**HEADPHONES**	**MAGAZINE**	**NEWSPAPER**	 **BOTTLED WATER**
BILLBOARD	**SPEED SIGN**	 **CAR**	**REST AREA**	 **MOTORCYCLE**
 **BRIDGE**	**BUS**	**SATELLITE DISH**	 **LAKE**	**FLAG**
 **TRAFFIC CONE**	**OUT OF STATE**	**GAS STATION**	 **FOREST**	 **POLICE CAR**

OUT AND ABOUT BINGO

 COFFEE HOUSE

 CELL PHONE

 BABY

 SKYLINE

 DOG

 CLOUD

 HEADPHONES

 MAGAZINE

 NEWSPAPER

 BOTTLED WATER

 BILLBOARD

 SPEED SIGN

 CAR

 REST AREA

 MOTORCYCLE

 BRIDGE

 BUS

 SATELLITE DISH

 LAKE

 FLAG

 TRAFFIC CONE

 OUT OF STATE

 GAS STATION

 FOREST

 POLICE CAR

OUT AND ABOUT BINGO

 COFFEE HOUSE	 **CELL PHONE**	 **BABY**	 **SKYLINE**	 **DOG**
 **CLOUD**	 **HEADPHONES**	 **MAGAZINE**	 **NEWSPAPER**	 **BOTTLED WATER**
 BILLBOARD	 **SPEED SIGN**	 **CAR**	 **REST AREA**	 **MOTORCYCLE**
 **BRIDGE**	 **BUS**	 **SATELLITE DISH**	 **LAKE**	 **FLAG**
 TRAFFIC CONE	 **OUT OF STATE**	 **GAS STATION**	 **FOREST**	 **POLICE CAR**

OUT AND ABOUT BINGO

COFFEE HOUSE	**CELL PHONE**	**BABY**	**SKYLINE**	**DOG**

CLOUD	**HEADPHONES**	**MAGAZINE**	**NEWSPAPER**	**BOTTLED WATER**

BILLBOARD	**SPEED SIGN**	**CAR**	**REST AREA**	**MOTORCYCLE**

BRIDGE	**BUS**	**SATELLITE DISH**	**LAKE**	**FLAG**

TRAFFIC CONE	**OUT OF STATE**	**GAS STATION**	**FOREST**	**POLICE CAR**

OUT AND ABOUT BINGO

 **COFFEE HOUSE**	**CELL PHONE**	 **BABY**	 **SKYLINE**	 **DOG**
CLOUD	**HEADPHONES**	**MAGAZINE**	**NEWSPAPER**	 **BOTTLED WATER**
BILLBOARD	**SPEED SIGN**	 **CAR**	**REST AREA**	 **MOTORCYCLE**
 **BRIDGE**	**BUS**	**SATELLITE DISH**	 **LAKE**	**FLAG**
 **TRAFFIC CONE**	**OUT OF STATE**	**GAS STATION**	 **FOREST**	 **POLICE CAR**

OUT AND ABOUT BINGO

COFFEE HOUSE	**CELL PHONE**	**BABY**	**SKYLINE**	**DOG**

CLOUD	**HEADPHONES**	**MAGAZINE**	**NEWSPAPER**	**BOTTLED WATER**

BILLBOARD	**SPEED SIGN**	**CAR**	**REST AREA**	**MOTORCYCLE**

BRIDGE	**BUS**	**SATELLITE DISH**	**LAKE**	**FLAG**

TRAFFIC CONE	**OUT OF STATE**	**GAS STATION**	**FOREST**	**POLICE CAR**

OUT AND ABOUT BINGO

COFFEE HOUSE	**CELL PHONE**	 **BABY**	 **SKYLINE**	 **DOG**
CLOUD	**HEADPHONES**	**MAGAZINE**	**NEWSPAPER**	 **BOTTLED WATER**
BILLBOARD	**SPEED SIGN**	 **CAR**	**REST AREA**	 **MOTORCYCLE**
 **BRIDGE**	**BUS**	**SATELLITE DISH**	 **LAKE**	**FLAG**
TRAFFIC CONE	**OUT OF STATE**	**GAS STATION**	**FOREST**	 **POLICE CAR**

OUT AND ABOUT BINGO

COFFEE HOUSE	**CELL PHONE**	**BABY**	**SKYLINE**	**DOG**

CLOUD	**HEADPHONES**	**MAGAZINE**	**NEWSPAPER**	**BOTTLED WATER**

BILLBOARD	**SPEED SIGN**	**CAR**	**REST AREA**	**MOTORCYCLE**

BRIDGE	**BUS**	**SATELLITE DISH**	**LAKE**	**FLAG**

TRAFFIC CONE	**OUT OF STATE**	**GAS STATION**	**FOREST**	**POLICE CAR**

OUT AND ABOUT BINGO

COFFEE HOUSE

CELL PHONE

BABY

SKYLINE

DOG

CLOUD

HEADPHONES

MAGAZINE

NEWSPAPER

BOTTLED WATER

BILLBOARD

SPEED SIGN

CAR

REST AREA

MOTORCYCLE

BRIDGE

BUS

SATELLITE DISH

LAKE

FLAG

TRAFFIC CONE

OUT OF STATE

GAS STATION

FOREST

POLICE CAR

OUT AND ABOUT BINGO

COFFEE HOUSE	CELL PHONE	BABY	SKYLINE	DOG

CLOUD	HEADPHONES	MAGAZINE	NEWSPAPER	BOTTLED WATER

BILLBOARD	SPEED SIGN	CAR	REST AREA	MOTORCYCLE

BRIDGE	BUS	SATELLITE DISH	LAKE	FLAG

TRAFFIC CONE	OUT OF STATE	GAS STATION	FOREST	POLICE CAR

OUT AND ABOUT BINGO

 **COFFEE HOUSE**	**CELL PHONE**	 **BABY**	 **SKYLINE**	 **DOG**
 **CLOUD**	 **HEADPHONES**	**MAGAZINE**	**NEWSPAPER**	 **BOTTLED WATER**
BILLBOARD	**SPEED SIGN**	 **CAR**	**REST AREA**	 **MOTORCYCLE**
 **BRIDGE**	**BUS**	**SATELLITE DISH**	 **LAKE**	**FLAG**
TRAFFIC CONE	**OUT OF STATE**	**GAS STATION**	 **FOREST**	 **POLICE CAR**

CONNECT 5

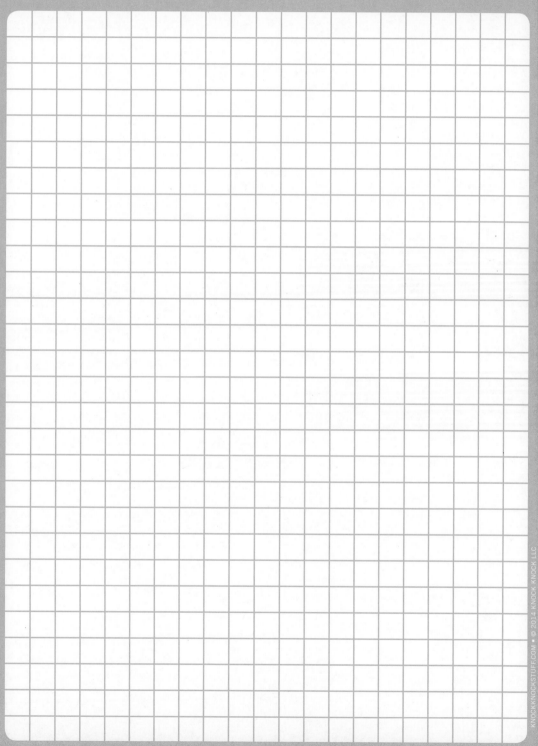

CONNECT 5

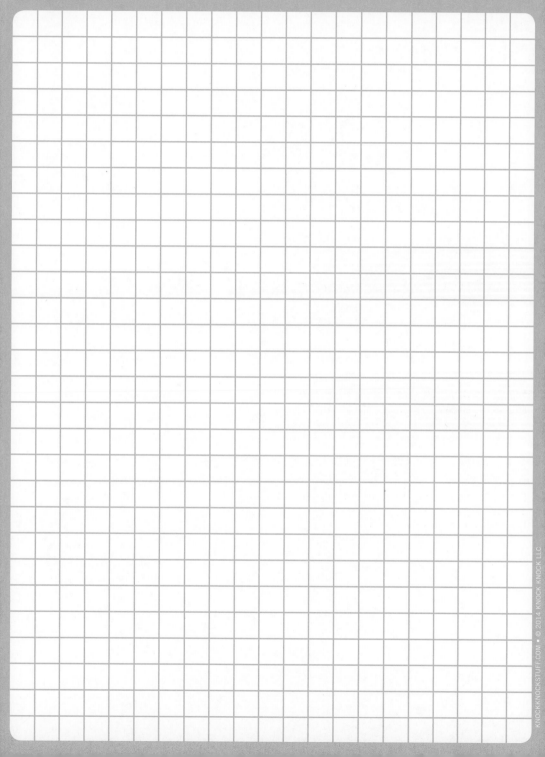

CONNECT 5

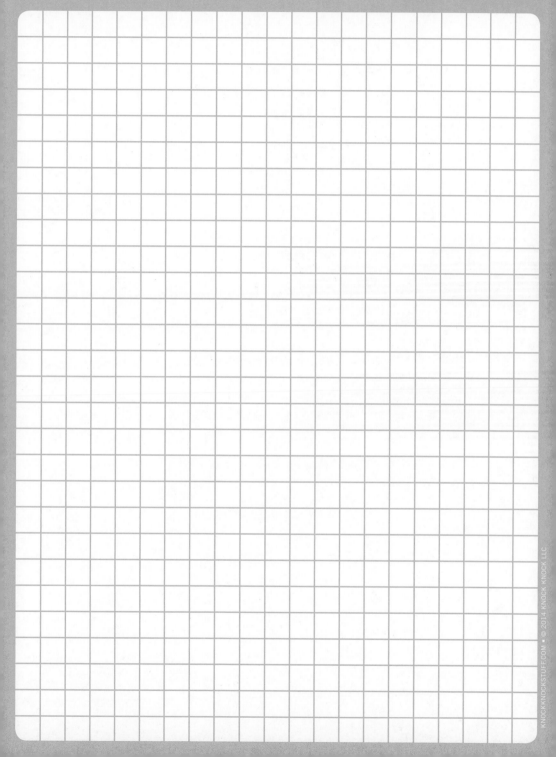

CONNECT 5

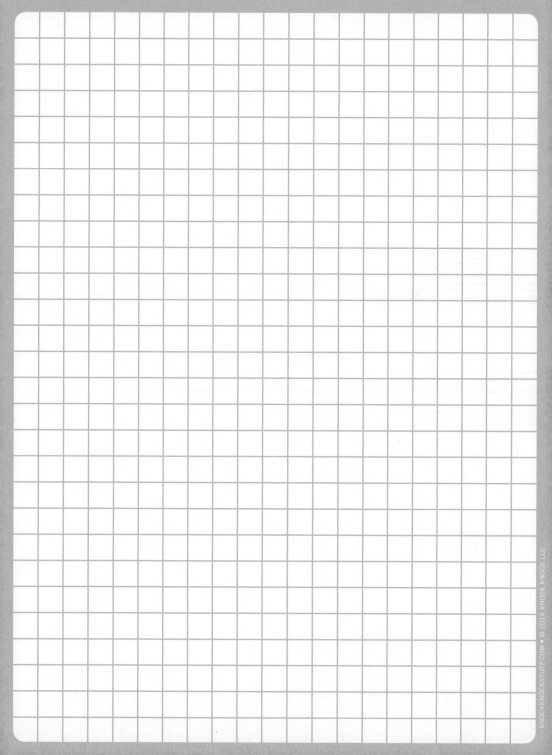

CONNECT 5

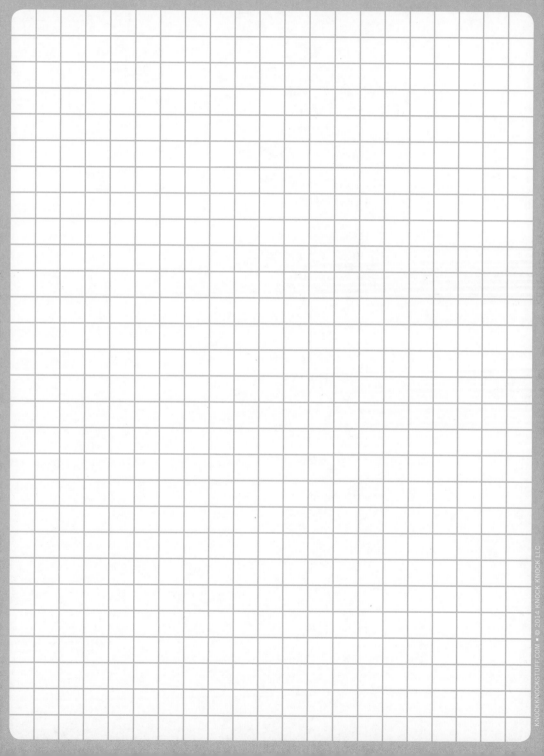

CONNECT 5

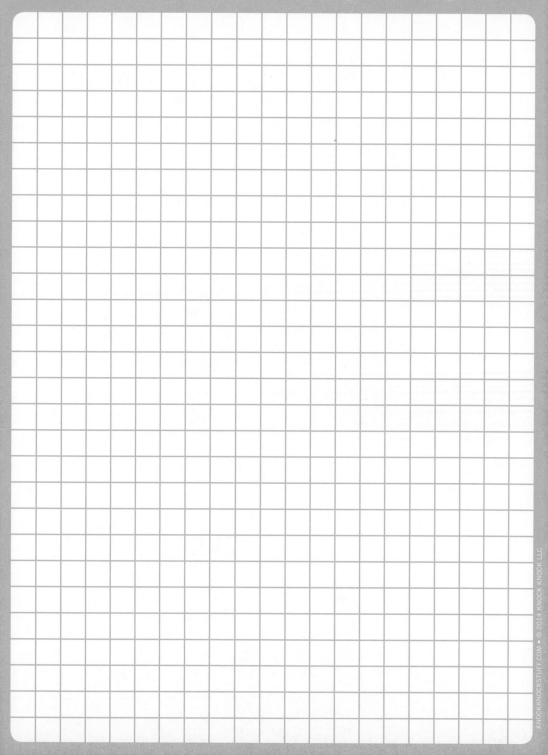

CONNECT 5

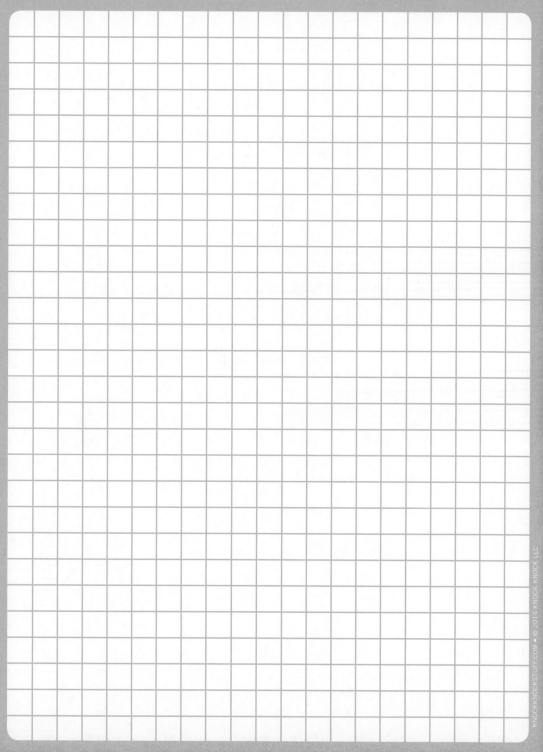

CONNECT 5

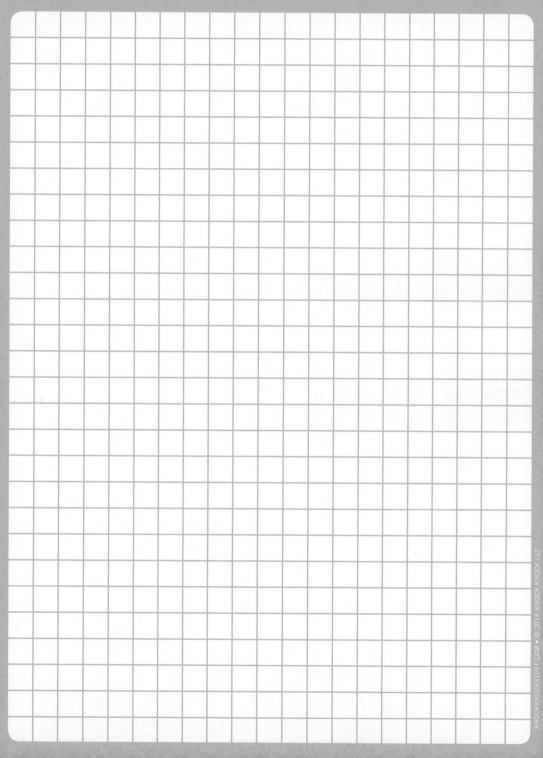

CONNECT 5

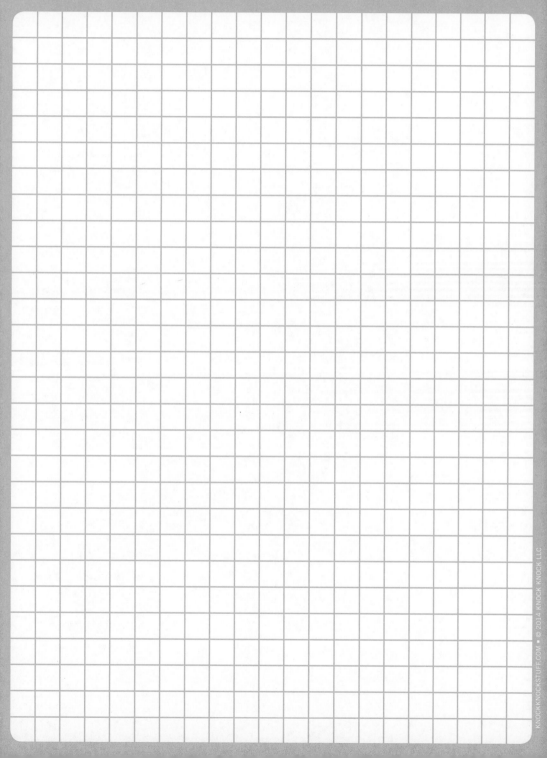

CONNECT 5

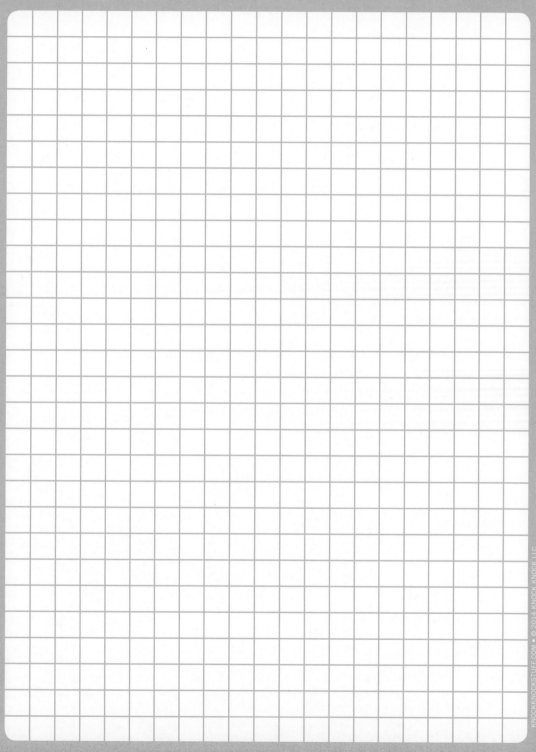

CONNECT 5

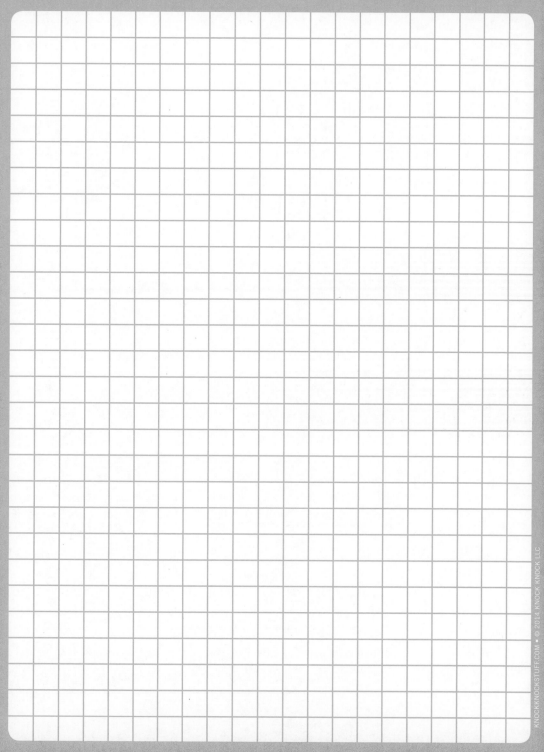

CONNECT 5

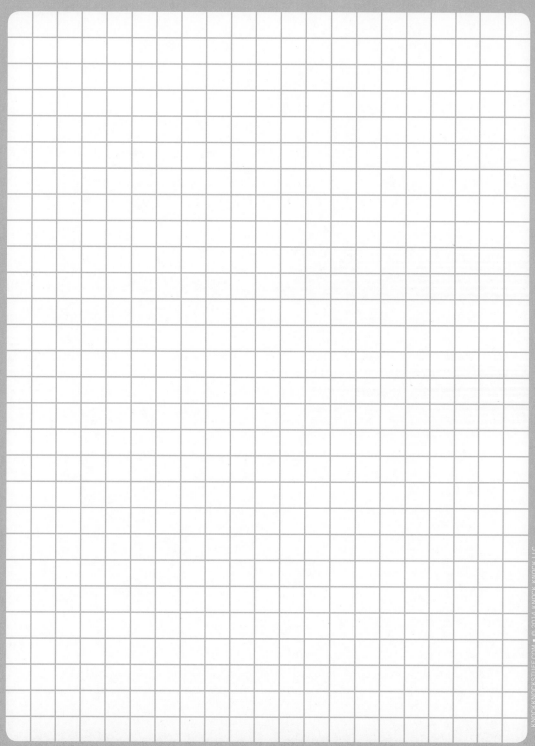

PICK 9

_____ _____ _____ _____ _____ _____ _____ _____ _____

1. _____
2. _____
3. _____
4. _____
5. _____
6. _____
7. _____
8. _____
9. _____
10. _____
11. _____
12. _____
13. _____
14. _____
15. _____

16. _____
17. _____
18. _____
19. _____
20. _____
21. _____
22. _____
23. _____
24. _____
25. _____
26. _____
27. _____
28. _____
29. _____
30. _____

PICK 9

_____ _____ _____ _____ _____ _____ _____ _____ _____

1. _____   16. _____

2. _____   17. _____

3. _____   18. _____

4. _____   19. _____

5. _____   20. _____

6. _____   21. _____

7. _____   22. _____

8. _____   23. _____

9. _____   24. _____

10. _____   25. _____

11. _____   26. _____

12. _____   27. _____

13. _____   28. _____

14. _____   29. _____

15. _____   30. _____

PICK 9

_____ _____ _____ _____ _____ _____ _____ _____ _____ _____ _____ _____

1. _____
2. _____
3. _____
4. _____
5. _____
6. _____
7. _____
8. _____
9. _____
10. _____
11. _____
12. _____
13. _____
14. _____
15. _____

16. _____
17. _____
18. _____
19. _____
20. _____
21. _____
22. _____
23. _____
24. _____
25. _____
26. _____
27. _____
28. _____
29. _____
30. _____

PICK 9

___ ___ ___ ___ ___ ___ ___ ___ ___ ___

1. _____
2. _____
3. _____
4. _____
5. _____
6. _____
7. _____
8. _____
9. _____
10. _____
11. _____
12. _____
13. _____
14. _____
15. _____
16. _____
17. _____
18. _____
19. _____
20. _____
21. _____
22. _____
23. _____
24. _____
25. _____
26. _____
27. _____
28. _____
29. _____
30. _____

PICK 9

_____ _____ _____ _____ _____ _____ _____ _____ _____

1. _____
2. _____
3. _____
4. _____
5. _____
6. _____
7. _____
8. _____
9. _____
10. _____
11. _____
12. _____
13. _____
14. _____
15. _____

16. _____
17. _____
18. _____
19. _____
20. _____
21. _____
22. _____
23. _____
24. _____
25. _____
26. _____
27. _____
28. _____
29. _____
30. _____

PICK 9

_____ _____ _____ _____ _____ _____ _____ _____ _____ _____ _____ _____

1. _____
2. _____
3. _____
4. _____
5. _____
6. _____
7. _____
8. _____
9. _____
10. _____
11. _____
12. _____
13. _____
14. _____
15. _____
16. _____
17. _____
18. _____
19. _____
20. _____
21. _____
22. _____
23. _____
24. _____
25. _____
26. _____
27. _____
28. _____
29. _____
30. _____

PICK 9

_____ _____ _____ _____ _____ _____ _____ _____ _____

1. _____
2. _____
3. _____
4. _____
5. _____
6. _____
7. _____
8. _____
9. _____
10. _____
11. _____
12. _____
13. _____
14. _____
15. _____

16. _____
17. _____
18. _____
19. _____
20. _____
21. _____
22. _____
23. _____
24. _____
25. _____
26. _____
27. _____
28. _____
29. _____
30. _____

PICK 9

_____ _____ _____ _____ _____ _____ _____ _____ _____

1. _____
2. _____
3. _____
4. _____
5. _____
6. _____
7. _____
8. _____
9. _____
10. _____
11. _____
12. _____
13. _____
14. _____
15. _____

16. _____
17. _____
18. _____
19. _____
20. _____
21. _____
22. _____
23. _____
24. _____
25. _____
26. _____
27. _____
28. _____
29. _____
30. _____

PICK 9

_____ _____ _____ _____ _____ _____ _____ _____ _____

1. _____
2. _____
3. _____
4. _____
5. _____
6. _____
7. _____
8. _____
9. _____
10. _____
11. _____
12. _____
13. _____
14. _____
15. _____
16. _____
17. _____
18. _____
19. _____
20. _____
21. _____
22. _____
23. _____
24. _____
25. _____
26. _____
27. _____
28. _____
29. _____
30. _____

PICK 9

_____ _____ _____ _____ _____ _____ _____ _____ _____

1. _____
2. _____
3. _____
4. _____
5. _____
6. _____
7. _____
8. _____
9. _____
10. _____
11. _____
12. _____
13. _____
14. _____
15. _____

16. _____
17. _____
18. _____
19. _____
20. _____
21. _____
22. _____
23. _____
24. _____
25. _____
26. _____
27. _____
28. _____
29. _____
30. _____

PICK 9

____ ____ ____ ____ ____ ____ ____ ____ ____

1. _____

2. _____

3. _____

4. _____

5. _____

6. _____

7. _____

8. _____

9. _____

10. _____

11. _____

12. _____

13. _____

14. _____

15. _____

16. _____

17. _____

18. _____

19. _____

20. _____

21. _____

22. _____

23. _____

24. _____

25. _____

26. _____

27. _____

28. _____

29. _____

30. _____

PICK 9

_____ _____ _____ _____ _____ _____ _____ _____ _____

1. _____
2. _____
3. _____
4. _____
5. _____
6. _____
7. _____
8. _____
9. _____
10. _____
11. _____
12. _____
13. _____
14. _____
15. _____

16. _____
17. _____
18. _____
19. _____
20. _____
21. _____
22. _____
23. _____
24. _____
25. _____
26. _____
27. _____
28. _____
29. _____
30. _____

PAPER GOLF

KEY:

- - - - - SAND TRAP
〜〜〜 WATER
I I I I I TREES

PAPER GOLF

KEY:

- - - - - SAND TRAP
~~~~~ WATER
I I I I I TREES

PAPER GOLF

KEY:

- - - - - SAND TRAP
〰〰〰 WATER
I I I I I TREES

PAPER GOLF

KEY:

- - - - - SAND TRAP
〜〜〜 WATER
I I I I I TREES

KEY:

----- SAND TRAP
〜〜〜 WATER
ı ı ı ı ı TREES

PAPER GOLF

KEY:

- - - - - SAND TRAP
≈≈≈ WATER
I I I I I TREES

PAPER GOLF

KEY:

- - - - - SAND TRAP
〜〜〜 WATER
I I I I I TREES

PAPER GOLF

KEY:

- - - - - SAND TRAP
~~~~~ WATER
I I I I I I TREES

PAPER GOLF

KEY:

- - - - - SAND TRAP
≈≈≈ WATER
I I I I I TREES

PAPER GOLF

KEY:

- - - - - SAND TRAP
~~~~~ WATER
| | | | | TREES

PAPER GOLF

KEY:

- - - - - SAND TRAP
~~~~~ WATER
| | | | | TREES

PAPER GOLF

KEY:

- - - - - SAND TRAP
〜〜〜 WATER
I I I I I TREES